My First Five Years

Images by

ANNE GEDDES

First published in Great Britain in 1995
by HEADLINE BOOK PUBLISHING

10 9 8 7 6 5 4 3 2 1

British Library Cataloguing in Publication Data
A catalogue record for this book is available from the British Library

ISBN 0 7472 1545 6

Designed by Jane Seabrook
Produced by Kel Geddes
Colour Separations by MH Imaging
Artwork by Bazz 'n' Else
Printed through Colorcraft, Hong Kong

HEADLINE BOOK PUBLISHING
A division of Hodder Headline PLC
338 Euston Road
London NW1 3BH

ANNE GEDDES

Anne Geddes, an Australian-born photographer, resident in Auckland, New Zealand, has won the hearts of people internationally with her unique and special images of children.

Not only is her work widely recognised and sought after in the commercial field, but her exceptional images have received resounding critical acclaim, attracting a host of professional awards.

Many of Anne's distinctive and memorable photographs have been published internationally, including the prestigious USA's *"Life"* Magazine, Germany's *"Tempo"*, the *"London Sunday Mirror"* and The News of the World *"Sunday Magazine"* to name but a few.

Anne's work mirrors the joy and love found in the children who will form the future of the planet. After all, she says, *"To be able to capture on film the innocence, trust and happiness that is inherent in the next generation is a very special responsibility. It's work that rewards me daily with a great deal of personal satisfaction."*

Another major challenge in Anne's life is to ensure that the photography of children is widely accepted as an art form that legitimately competes with any other form of photographic speciality.

Anne is married to her friend and business partner Kel. Together they have two children.

Contents

My Birth

My Name is

Daniel Sebastian Stanley

I was born on _Tuesday 5 September 1925_

at _Stirling Royal Infirmary_

The time was _9·55 am_

I was delivered by _____

_____

I weighed  _7 lbs 11 oz_

and measured

60 centimetres

My eyes were _dark blue_

My hair was _dark blond_

Mementos

My Birth Announcement

A lock of hair

My hospital tag

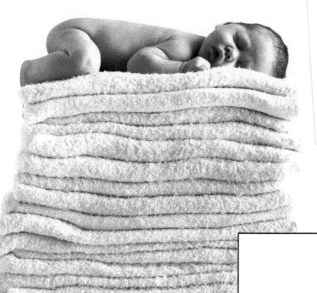

Newspaper Clippings

What was happening in the world

Photographs

Comments

Mother_____

_____

_____

_____

Father_____

_____

_____

Special Messages

Family _____

_____

_____

_____

_____

Friends _____

_____

_____

_____

_____

Visitors and Gifts

14

Signs

Star Sign _____

_____

Chinese Year _____

_____

Birth Stone _____

_____

Birth Flower

_____

Naming

My full name is _Daniel, Sebastian, Stanley_

My name was chosen by _my mum and dad_

because _they liked the name Daniel and thought it suited me and they were both fans of Seb Coe._

My pet names are _Danny and ZinZam after ZinZam Brookes the All Blacks No 8._

I was christened on _____

at _____

Comments _____

_____

_____

_____

Photographs

My Family Tree

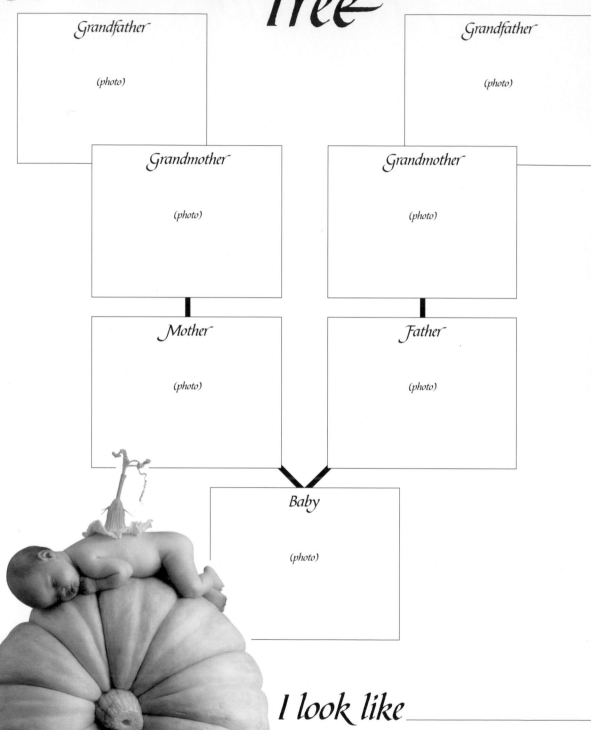

Grandfather

(photo)

Grandfather

(photo)

Grandmother

(photo)

Grandmother

(photo)

Mother

(photo)

Father

(photo)

Baby

(photo)

I look like _____

_____

Photographs

Brothers and Sisters

Three Months

Weight _____

Length _____

Comments

_____

_____

_____

_____

Photographs

Six Months

Weight _____ Length _____

Comments _____

_____

_____

_____

_____

Photographs

Nine Months

Weight _____

Length _____

Comments _____

_____

_____

_____

_____

_____

_____

Photographs

Milestones

I first smiled _____

laughed _____

grasped a toy _____

I slept through the night

_____

I held my head up _at two days old_ _____

rolled over _____

sat up _____

Comments _____

_____

_____

I first crawled _____

stood up _____ walked _____

My first tooth _____

My first word _____

_____

Comments

_____

_____

_____

_____

Food

My first solid food _____

I was weaned _____

I drank from a cup _____

Finger food _____

I fed myself _____

I like _____

_____

_____

_____

_____

I don't like _____

_____

_____

_____

_____

My First
Christmas

was at _____

Other people there

_____

_____

_____

My presents

_____

_____

_____

Photographs

My First Holiday

Was at _____

Date _____

The weather was _____

Other people there _____

_____

_____

Comments

_____

_____

_____

Photographs

My First
Birthday

I live at _____

_____

My height is _____

Weight _____

Sayings _____

_____

Toys _____

Pets _____

Books _____

_____

My Party

Date _____

Where held _____

Friends and relations there _____

_____

_____

_____

My presents _____

_____

_____

_____

Photographs

Clothes

The first time I dressed myself

_____

I wore _____

My favourite dress-ups _____

_____

_____

I won't wear _____

_____

_____

Comments _____

_____

Photographs

Favourites

Music _____

_____

_____

_____

Rhymes _____

_____

Clothes _____

_____

Animals _____

_____

_____

Activities _____

_____

_____

Television Programmes _____

_____

_____

_____

I really don't like _____

_____

_____

_____

Best Friends

One Year

RESERVED FOR SAM RIDDLE

photo

Two Years

RESERVED FOR SAM RIDDLE

photo

Comments _____

_____

_____

_____

Three Years

THAT'S ME AGAIN

photo

Comments _____

_____

_____

_____

Four Years

I'M STILL YOUR BEST
FRIEND

photo

Five Years

I'M YOUR BESTEST FRIEND

LOVE
SAM **

photo

_____

_____

_____

_____

My Second Birthday

I live at _____

My height is _____ Weight _____

Sayings _____

Toys _____

_____

Pets _____

_____

Books _____

_____

_____

My Party

Date _____

Where held _____

Friends and relations there

_____

_____

_____

_____

My presents _____

_____

_____

_____

Photographs

My Third Birthday

I live at _____

My height is _____ Weight _____

Sayings _____

_____

Toys _____

Pets _____

Books _____

_____

_____

_____

My Party

Date _____

Where held _____

Friends and relations there _____

_____

_____

_____

_____

My presents

_____

_____

49

Photographs

Kindergarten

I started on _____

at _____

My friends are _____

_____

Comments _____

_____

_____

_____

_____

Photographs

My Fourth Birthday

I live at _____

_____

My height is _____

Weight _____

Sayings _____

_____

_____

Toys _____

Pets _____

Books _____

My Party

Date _____

Where held _____

Friends and relations there _____

_____

_____

_____

_____

My presents _____

_____

_____

_____

Photographs

My Fifth Birthday

I live at _____

My height is _____ Weight _____

Sayings _____

Toys _____

_____

Pets _____

_____

Books _____

_____

_____

My Party

Date_____

Where held_____

_____

Friends and relations there

_____

_____

My presents_____

_____

_____

_____

Photographs

School

My first day at school was on _____

_____ at _____

My teacher is _____

Comments _____

A _____

_____

B _____

_____

C D E F

Photographs

Drawings

O_{h no!} P Q R

Writing

I could recite the alphabet _____

_____

I started to write _____

I began to read _____

My writing _____

_____

_____

_____

_____

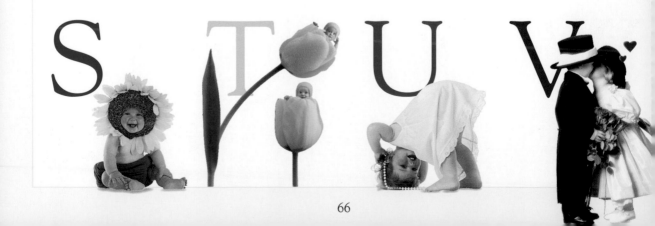

W X Y Z

Immunisation

Age	Vaccine	Date given

Allergies

_____

_____
_____

_____

Illnesses

_____

_____

_____

Comments

_____

_____
_____

_____

My Height

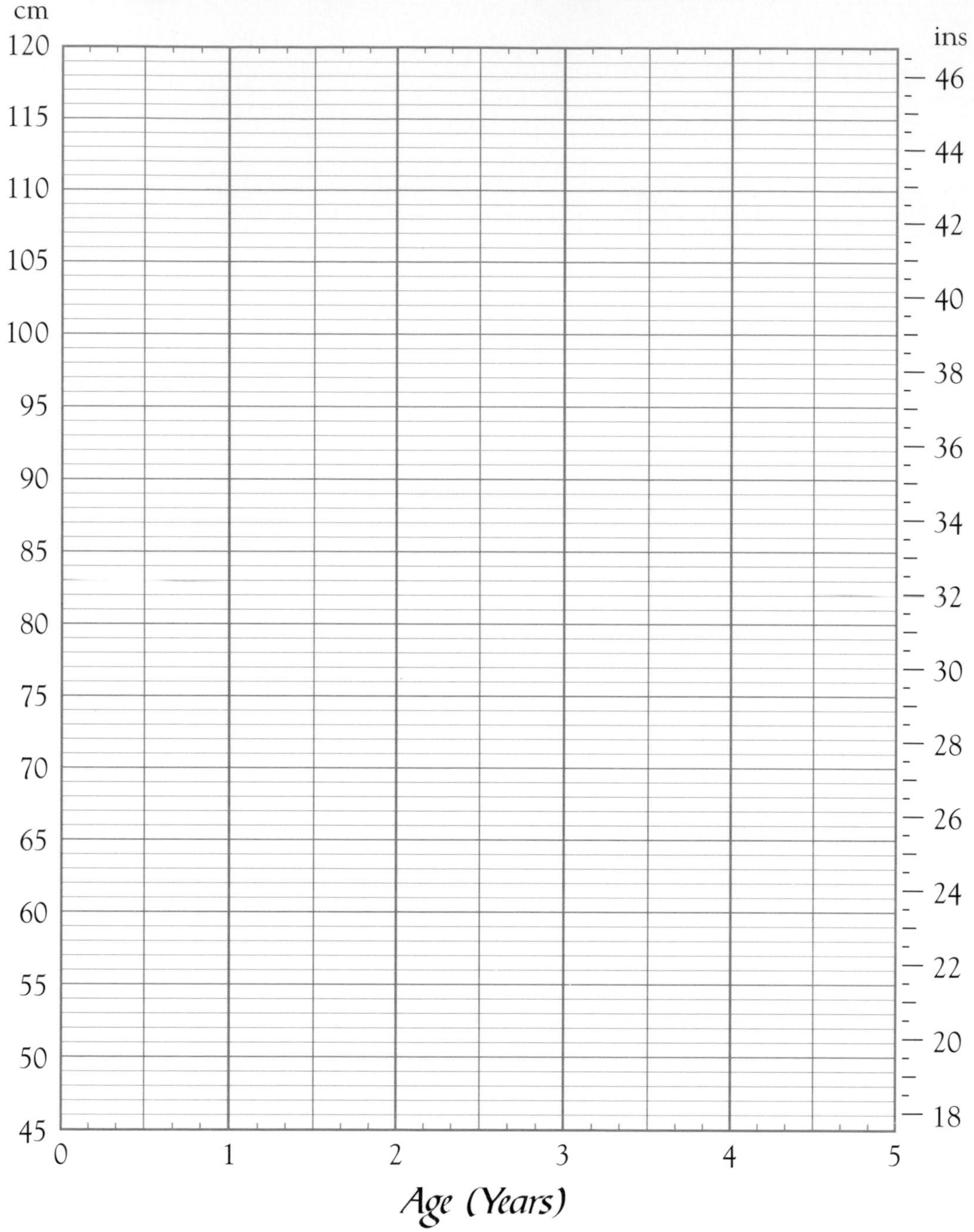
cm
120
115
110
105
100
95
90
85
80
75
70
65
60
55
50
45
ins
46
44
42
40
38
36
34
32
30
28
26
24
22
20
18
0
1
2
3
4
5
Age (Years)

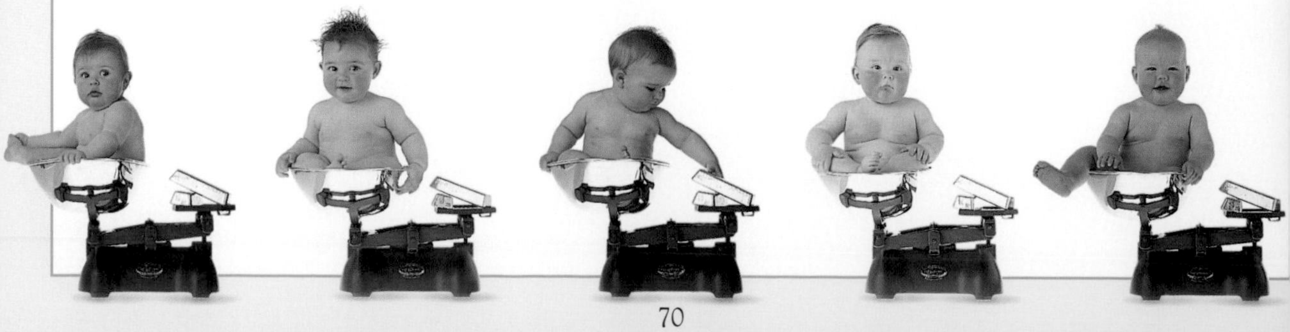

My Weight

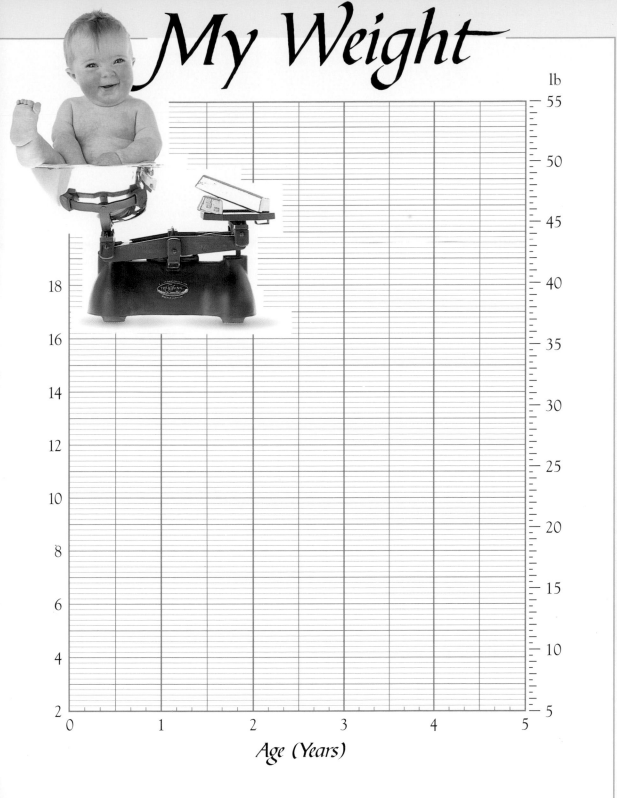

Age (Years)

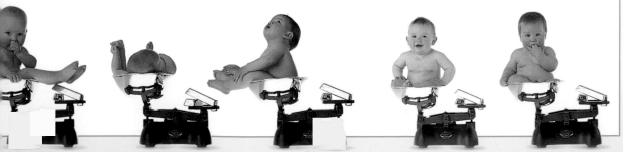

My Teeth

Upper Jaw

Date

8
9
16
13
24

Months

24
13
16
10
7

Date

Lower Jaw

Dental Nurse visits _____

The Tooth Fairy's page

I lost my first tooth on _____

My second tooth _____

The Tooth Fairy left me_____

_____

Comments _____

_____

_____

_____

My Handprints

At birth

At five years

My Footprints

At birth

At five years

Star Signs

Capricorn
22 December – 20 January
Resourceful, self-sufficient, responsible

Aquarius
21 January – 18 February
Great caring for others, very emotional
under cool exterior

Pisces
19 February – 19 March
Imaginative, sympathetic, tolerant

Aries
20 March – 20 April
Brave, courageous, energetic, loyal

Taurus
21 April – 21 May
Sensible, love peace and stability

Gemini
22 May – 21 June
Unpredictable, lively, charming, witty

Cancer
22 June – 22 July
Love security, comfort

Leo
23 July – 23 August
Idealistic, romantic, honourable, loyal

Virgo
24 August – 23 September
Shy, sensitive, value knowledge

Libra
24 September – 23 October
Diplomat, full of charm and style

Scorpio
24 October – 22 November
Compassionate, proud, determined

Sagittarius
23 November – 21 December
Bold, impulsive, seek adventure

Birth Stones

January	Garnet – Constancy and truth
February	Amethyst – Sincerity, humility
March	Aquamarine – Courage and energy
April	Diamond – Innocence, success
May	Emerald – Tranquillity
June	Pearl – Precious, pristine
July	Ruby – Freedom from care, chastity
August	Moonstone – Joy
September	Sapphire – Hope, chastity
October	Opal – Reflects every mood
November	Topaz – Fidelity, loyalty
December	Turquoise – Love and success

Flowers

January	Snowdrop – Pure and gentle
February	Carnation – Bold and brave
March	Violet – Modest
April	Lily – Virtuous
May	Hawthorn – Bright and hopeful
June	Rose – Beautiful
July	Daisy – Wide-eyed and innocent
August	Poppy – Peaceful
September	Morning Glory – Easily contented
October	Cosmos – Ambitious
November	Chrysanthemum – Cheeky and cheerful
December	Holly – Full of foresight

Comments

Photographs

Comments

Photographs